NOAH's ARK

by
Lindy Norton

© THE MEDICI SOCIETY LTD · LONDON · 1989 *Printed in England* ISBN 0 85503 155 7

God, long ago, viewed the World with regret,
His hopes were all dashed – expectations not met,
These men were now evil, their natures were mean,
Enough of their fighting and lying He'd seen,
'I'll destroy all that's flesh!' is what God decreed,
'It's more than a scolding that these sinners need.'

But Noah was different, he was a good man,
And would, God decided, fulfil His grand plan,

'Build a great Ark on which you will stay;
Take your wife with your children and start straight away.'

So God gave instructions on style and dimensions,
To build the best vessel to fulfil his intentions,

'We will now need a pair of each living thing,
The creeping, the slithering and birds of the wing'.

Elephants, panda bears, buffalo and goats,

Llamas, zebras, monkeys and stoats,

Camels and tigers, turkeys and mice,

All equally welcomed, even the lice.

The turtles came slowly, and so did the snails,

Then seals and crocodiles dragging their tails,

The Ark was now full, two of each were collected,

Noah shut the door, no beast was neglected.

Plip, one drop of rain, *Plop* there were two,
The sky clouded over, and turned a dark blue,

The Heavens then opened, water covered the Earth,
It rained and it rained for all it was worth.

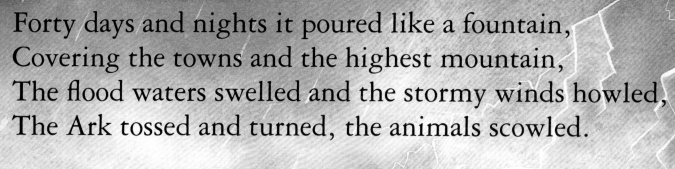

Forty days and nights it poured like a fountain,
Covering the towns and the highest mountain,
The flood waters swelled and the stormy winds howled,
The Ark tossed and turned, the animals scowled.

Inside the Ark the creatures grew restless,
Dogs barked, chicks squawked,
                    the cheetahs were listless,
Horses were stamping, the fox was confused,
Noah tried a few jokes to keep them amused.

Noah despaired, the Ark was in riot.
Then Elephant shouted, 'PLEASE, everyone quiet,'

The Ark fell silent, you could hear a pin drop,
Noah opened the window, 'The raining has STOPPED.'

Noah sent forth a dove, she found nowhere to rest,
He waited a while, he thought that was best,
Again she flew forth, but came back excited,
With a fresh olive leaf, DRY LAND she had sighted!

The land dried up, not one cloud in sight,
All sin washed away so the World was put right,

The Ark door was opened for the animals to leave,
Chatting and laughing, with sighs of relief.

The sun beamed down – such a glorious day!
God sent them a rainbow, as a promise, to say,
'Never again will I send such flood waters,
So please tell your children, your sons and your daughters,
This lesson you've learned, this ordeal you've survived,
Shall good conquer evil? It's for you to decide!'